Barnaby's trip to Dublin

BELFAST

IRISH SEA

Manchester

Liverpool

DUBLIN

⊕ Manchester Airport

Chester

Liz Lewis

Geographical
Association

CARDIFF

Barnaby Bear is
going to Dublin.

The taxi takes Barnaby to the airport.

At the airport Barnaby has to show his ticket.

Barnaby goes up and up in the plane.

When Barnaby gets to the hotel he looks at his map of Dublin.

Where shall I go?

Phoenix Park

Dublin Zoo

Parnell Square

Route of Grand Tour

River

Liffey

General Post Office

O'Connell Street

Custom House

HA'PENNY BRIDGE

O'CONNELL BRIDGE

Temple Bar Area

Dublin Castle

Grafton Street

Trinity College

Merrion Square

0   5
km

Barnaby sees lots of animals at Dublin Zoo.

Penguins

Elephants

Monkeys

Meerkats

Giraffes

Next Barnaby goes shopping. It is very busy.

Dublin
17 April

Dear Mum and Dad

I like it in Dublin. Today
I have been shopping
and I am going to the
park.

Love
Barnaby xxx

ÉIRE 30

Mr and Mrs Bear

5 Elaine Street

CHESTER

CH64 7TQ

ENGLAND

Barnaby writes a postcard to send to his
Mum and Dad. He posts it in a green
post box.

9

Barnaby goes to the park.

He plays on the slide and the swings.

Now it is time for Barnaby to go home.